This book was born from a very real question-
How can we reach children today in a way that models
and inspires both gratitude and empathy? "Thankful" is
our answer. We knew when writing this song that we
were dancing on the edge of igniting real change. When
we first played "Thankful" for the children in our school
communities, we were overwhelmed by the joy that simply
talking and singing about thankfulness elicited. There
was no shortage of people, places, or ideas the children
shared- with the dominant theme being family. We chose
to continue to honor this mission of fostering gratitude
by extending our message to a broader audience-
you and your family.

The illustrations and main text follow the
"Thankful" lyrics. In addition, we have included activities
and bonuses to help extend the conversation amongst
families. Some of the activities and bonuses require
families to venture outdoors, creatively imagine and
authentically reflect on the many joys and blessings
surrounding us.

Another dimension of this book fosters empathy
through a celebration of diversity. Today's children are
tomorrow's leaders and helping them embody empathy
when relating to others is our hope for a more peaceful
world. We believe that a first step in realizing this vision
is to encourage children to understand that within the
differences between us are the threads of what unite us.

To access the "Thankful" jam-along song you can
stream from the music tab at www.jamtreestudios.com
or download from your computer at-
www.jamtreestudios.com/jamalong/.

For the families of
Ravhi Bear and Monkey J.
We're so thankful for you
every single day!

Lyrics & Music:
Frank Jurado & Ravhi Demello
Text: Frank Jurado
Illustrations: Ravhi Demello

"Hello friends,
we're happy you are here!"

Ravhi Bear and Monkey J
jam together every day.
With their friends and family,
they gather by the old Jam Tree.

And in a circle, big and round,
so everyone can hear the sound,
they sit together on the floor
and share the things they're thankful for.

"Let's use our imagination and sing about all the things we're thankful for!"

Activity- Sing along with the "Thankful" song and think about all the things that bring you joy.

*Bonus- When you sing the word THANKFUL make the sign language motion like Ravhi Bear.

I'm thankful for all that we have.

Tiger, lemur, monkey and bear
are thankful for the things they share.
Sunshine, smiles and perfect weather
are so much fun to share together.

I'm thankful for all that we share.

Activity- Wave your arms in the air like the lemur.

Pretend to skateboard like Ravhi Bear and Monkey J.

*Bonus- Name your favorite things to share.

Try to share something every day.

I'm thankful for sunshine,

the stars,

and the rainbows.

Rainbows, stars and happy clouds-
the sun is smiling, looking proud.
Colors paint the skies above-
a canopy of light and love.

I'm thankful for clouds and for the air.

Activity- Draw a rainbow.

Underneath it draw three things that you love.

*Bonus (outside)- When you see a rainbow, say thanks to

the sun and rain for the beautiful colors they make together.

Thank you for all of your smiles.

Thank you for playing pretend.

Friends will play and friends will share.
Friends will smile to show they care.
Friends will laugh and play pretend.
I'm so thankful you're my friend.

Thank you for sharing your toys and your sandwiches.
Thank you for being my friend!

Activity- Look in a mirror and try to copy all of
the different smiles on the smiles page.
*Bonus- Name all of the friends that you are thankful for. Next
time you see them tell them you are thankful for their friendship.

I'm so thankful for the flowers and the bees,

for the birds and for the trees,

Flowers, bees, birds and trees-
leaves are swirling through the breeze.
Music here and music there.
Can you hear it in the air?

for the rhythm of the leaves...

that dance together,

Activity- Buzz like a bee. Stretch your arms to the sky like long tree branches. Let your fingers dance like leaves in the wind.

*Bonus (outside)- Next time you hear a bird singing, copy the sounds and listen for them to sing back.

for the simple melodies, for the music in the breeze,

Whistling winds and waves that crash-
colors mixing with a splash.
Mother Nature's melody-
played on land and sky and sea.

for the oceans and the seas
that come together!

Activity- Use your hands to copy the movement of the wind
and the waves. Use two hands to make the waves crash together.
*Bonus- Use crayons or paint and mix different colors to create your
own. Give your color a special name.

Sleepy moon and starry night,
soaring seagulls take to flight.
Owls sing so peacefully,
perched on branches in the trees.

Activity- bring your thumbs together and
use your fingers to fly like a bird.
*Bonus- Use a bright light in a dark room to make
shadow puppet animals on the wall.

Thank you for all that you are.
Thank you for being so strong.

Mom and baby, face to face,
snuggling in a warm embrace.
Different creatures, different names-
a mother's love feels just the same.

I'm thankful you care for me.
Thanks for being there for me.

Thank you for being my mom.

Activity- Use your arm like an elephant trunk and make
your best elephant call. Pretend to gently cradle a baby in your
arms and sing your favorite lullabye.

*Bonus- Give hugs to your family and the ones you love.

Thank you for all that you've done.
Thanks for the good times we've had.

Skies of blue and fields of green-
spending time without a screen.
Taking care and having fun-
a father's work is never done

Thank you for being the one I can lean on.

Thank you for being my dad!

Activity- Read and share your favorite
book with a friend or family member.
*Bonus (outside)- Bring your favorite book to the park,
kick off your shoes and feel the grass
between your toes while you read.

I'm so thankful for the blessings
and the joy that we receive...

All together drums and strings-
everybody plays and sings.
Ukulele, saxophone-
when we jam we're not alone.

if we just believe that we can come together.

Activity- Play these air instruments: guitar, drums, bass, ukulele and saxophone to your favorite song.

*Bonus- Use your whole body as an instrument. Clap your hands, stomp your feet, snap your fingers and bang on your chest.

Let our differences become our greatest gifts.

No two players look the same-
being different wins the game.
Reaching for the stars and sky-
friendship lifts their hearts up high.

Let's use them to uplift our hearts
and grow together!

Activity- Put your hand on your chest and
feel the rhythm of your heart beat.
*Bonus- All the teammates are different.
Name the things they have in common.

Thankful minds and thankful hearts,
thankful music, thankful art.
Thankful words and thankful voices,
thankful actions, thankful choices.

Thankful mornings, thankful nights-
Thankfulness is always right.
Thankful monkeys, thankful bears-
thankfulness is everywhere!

I'm so thankful, I'm so thankful, I'm so thankful!

stay together

stay together

grow together

Activity- Find the hidden Ukulele.
It looks like this-

Bonus- Look at the pictures to the right.
Can you spot the differences?

Thankful

By: Ravhi Bear & Monkey J

Verse 1

```
F#                                    B
    I'm thankful for all that we have
F#                                    C#
    I'm thankful for all that we share
        F#                 B
    I'm thankful for sunshine, the stars and the rainbows
G#m                         C#
    I'm thankful for clouds and for the air
F#                            B
    Thank you for all of your smiles
F#                            C#
    Thank you for playing pretend
F#                            B
    Thank you for sharing your toys and your sandwiches
G#m                          C#
    Thank you for being my friend
```

Pre-Chorus

```
        F#            B
    I'm so thankful for the flowers and the bees
        G#m
    For birds and for the trees or the
C#                                    F#
    rhythm of the leaves that dance together
        B                      G#m
    For the simple melodies, for the music in the breeze
        C#                         F#
    For the oceans and the seas that come together
```

Chorus

```
F#                 B           G#m        C#
    I'm so thankful, I'm so thankful, I'm so thankful
```

For the harmonies we make together
```
F#                        B              G#m           C#
```
    I'm so thankful, I'm so thankful, I'm so thankful

Verse 2
```
F#                                    B
```
    Thank you for all the you are
```
F#                                    C#
```
    Thank you for being so strong
```
         F#              B
```
    I'm thankful you care for me, thanks for being there for me
```
G#m                         C#
```
    Thank you being my mom
```
F#                                        B
```
    Thank you for all that you've done
```
F#                                      C#
```
    Thanks for the good times we had
```
F#                          B
```
    Thank you for being the one I can lean on
```
G#m                             C#
```
    Thank you for being my dad

Pre-Chorus
```
       F#              B                          G#m
```
    I'm so thankful for the blessings and the joy that we receive,
```
                   C#                    F#
```
    If we just believe that we can come together
```
             B                          G#m
```
    And let our differences become our greatest gifts
```
                    C#                          F#
```
    Lets use them to uplift our hearts and grow together

Chorus
```
F#              B              G#m           C#
```
    I'm so thankful, I'm so thankful, I'm so thankful
```
F#              B              G#m           C#
```
    I'm so thankful, I'm so thankful, I'm so thankful   X9

Special thanks to all of our school friends
and faculty for their support and
inspiration throughout
the creation of this book.

Made in the USA
San Bernardino, CA
28 October 2017